HORIZONS

Learning to Read

Fast Track A–B
Workbook 2

Siegfried Engelmann
Owen Engelmann
Karen Lou Seitz Davis

SRA/McGraw-Hill
Columbus, Ohio

Illustration credits

Dave Blanchette, Cindy Brodie, Daniel Clifford, Susanne Demarco, Daniel Del Valle, Pam Faessler, Kersti Frigell, Ethel Gold, Meryl Henderson, Ann Iosa, Susan Jerde, Anne Kennedy, Loretta Lustig, Louis Pappas, Pat Schories, Jeff Severn, Charles Shaw

SRA/McGraw-Hill

A Division of The **McGraw·Hill** *Companies*

Send all inquiries to:
SRA/McGraw-Hill
8787 Orion Place
Columbus, Ohio 43240-4027

ISBN 0-02-687507-1

7 8 9   DBH   04 03 02

Name _____

sit   sick   mole   r<u>ea</u>d   g<u>oa</u>t   ant

I feel _____.

You need to _____
and _____.

Note for goat.

goat   to   so   no   to | d<u>o</u> | go |
goat   go   so
no   goat   go   do   so
to   do   go   no   do   go   to
goat   do   go   no   to   no   so
goat   to   so   goat   go   go   to

e̲at   sap   s̲o̲ap   fly

fiv**e**

e̲ar

nin**e**

G •   • r
R •   • h
B •   • g
D •   • d
H •   • b

Name _____

coat   crow   fits   goat   it

No _____ can fit
in this _____.

May I see if
_____
_____ _____?

say   may   day
ray   win   say
win   do   pin   sail   say
win   say   in   said

~~win~~	(say)
3	4

mad r<u>ai</u>n m<u>ai</u>l
seeds t<u>o</u>ad cave

cake •   • came

make •   • kick

came •   • hike

hike •   • cake

kick •   • make

Side 2

Name _____

hit   hike   dad   fly   mile   crow

I hate to _____

so I will _____.

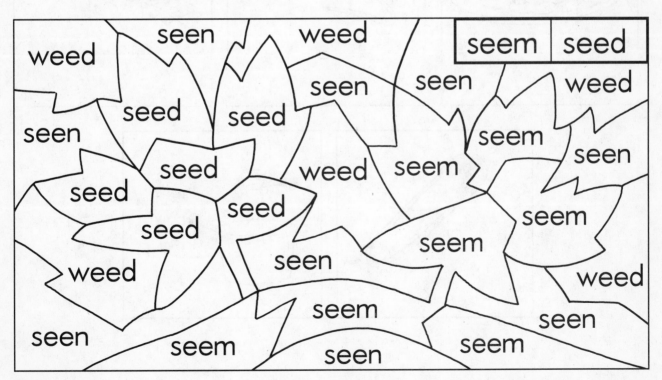

weed   seen   weed   seem   seed

seen   seed   seed   seen   weed

seed   seen   seem   seem

seed   weed   seem   seem

seed   seed   seem

weed   seen   seem

seen   seem   seen   seem   weed

seem   seen

pan pin pans pins
tr<u>ai</u>n tr<u>ai</u>l weed cake

Side 2

Name _____

fly crow home ant t<u>ai</u>l

I need to go _____ .

Hold my _____ and

we will _____ .

an •　　• ant

sand •　　• hand

hand •　　• an

ant •　　• and

and •　　• sand

| meal　nail　mail | m~~ai~~l | (m<u>ea</u>l) |
| rail　mole　meat | 2 | 4 |

nail　mean　meal　real　　sail

seal　　meal　mill　　mail　　tail

mole　　fail　　nail　　meal

s<u>p</u>y　　p<u>ig</u>　　<u>ea</u>r　　t<u>ai</u>l

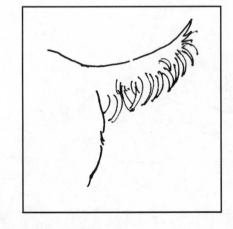

_____　　　　_____

_____　　　　_____

Name _____

stones   seal   came   cave   wave

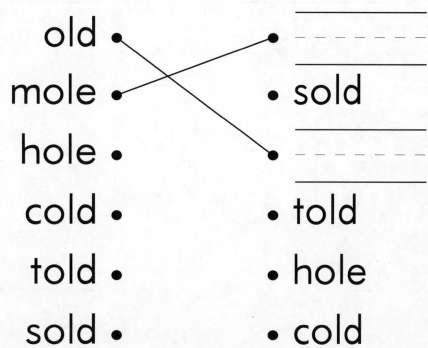

old •   • _____

mole •   • sold

hole •   • _____

cold •   • told

told •   • hole

sold •   • cold

game   j<u>ai</u>l   rak<u>e</u>

___ man

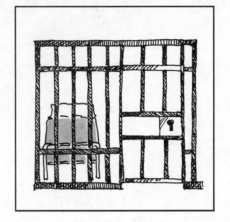

_____

p<u>ai</u>ls

_____

_____

stones

Side 2

This joke made
the rat mad.

fold

The Mole and
the Rat

A mole and a rat
like to play.

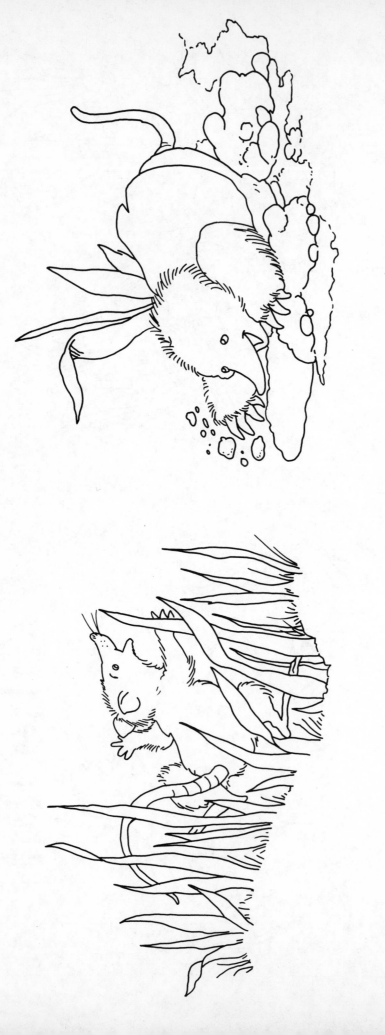

The mole likes to
play jokes.

The rat likes to
play in the weeds.

Name _____

toad   home   mole   here

Leave my _____.

No. I like it _____.

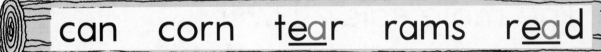

can   corn   tear   rams   read

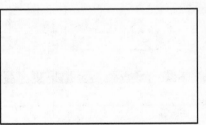

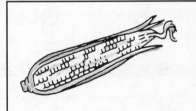

rope

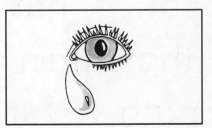

tree

1. A mole had a fine _____ .

| here | hold | home |

2. The mole told the t<u>o</u>ad
_____
to _____ .

| sit | l<u>ea</u>ve | l<u>ea</u>p |

3. The mole s<u>ai</u>d, "I will _____ ."

| go | st<u>ay</u> | sleep |

tail that path	t~~hat~~	(p<u>ai</u>l)
fat hat pal	3	2

that   pain   pail   tail   than

path   fat   that   pat   pail

Name _____

Five cats had fun at a lake.

n<u>ai</u>l   g<u>oa</u>t   tree

____ ____ <u>smile</u> ____

train •   • trip
trail •   • tree
trip •   • trail
tree •   • train

---

1. Five cats had fun at a _____.

| home | lake | cave |

---

2. 2 cats run up a _____.

| hill | tree | lake |

---

3. A cat sat in _____.

| the sun | a tree | a kite |

Name _____

crow   hay   mole   hid

We _____ in the _____.

1. A g<u>oa</u>t ate a _____.

| bug | m<u>ea</u>l | c<u>oa</u>t |

2. The g<u>oa</u>t told the crow t<u>o</u>

_____

_____

| hide n<u>ea</u>r trees | | hide in h<u>ay</u> |

_____ cans _____

can _____ _____

way •   • you

dry •   • way

fly •   • dry

stay •   • fly

you •   • _____

by •   • _____

Name _____

We can _____ .

tree
fly
t<u>ai</u>l
kite

crow   tape   names   sad

rug   home

      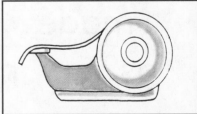

1. Al told his pals, "We_____."

| can fly | will sleep | need a m<u>e</u>al |

2. Al and his pals ran t<u>o</u> _____.

| a pile | a kite | a ram |

3. Al and his pals grabb<u>ed</u> _____.

| the t<u>ai</u>l | the fly | an <u>e</u>ar |

us   mud   is

mad   an   as   at

made   mud   is

as   mile   an   us   at

is   an   mud   mad

~~mud~~	(as)
3	2

Name _____

1. _____   2. _____

3. _____   4. _____

A cat ate a cake in a store. That cake was in a pan. The cat said, "I like to eat cake. I hate to eat stones."

A goat _____ a kite. Al the ant is _____.

fold

A G<u>oa</u>t
Likes to <u>E</u>at

Side 1

1. kick<u>ed</u>   1. hill   1. has
2. green   2. run   2. s<u>o</u>me
3. dug   3. ov<u>er</u>   3. d<u>o</u>
4. big   4. smil<u>ed</u>   4. fr<u>o</u>m

A g<u>oa</u>t ate a note.
The mole is mad.

A g<u>oa</u>t ate a c<u>oa</u>t.
The crow is mad.

Side 2

Name _____

five   mud   of   path   Bob

I see a hill of _____.

1. Bob had to come home by _____.

| nine | five | three |

2. Bob and his pals came to a
_____
_____.

| hill of mud | lake | pile of hay |

cat	bug	feet
van	tr<u>ay</u>	plane

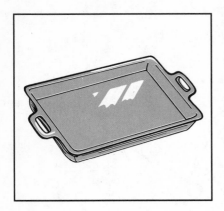
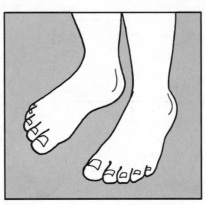

come •   • some

some •   • come

home •   • sun

sun •   • slid

slid •   • home

Side 2

Name

of   mud   Bob

We like this hill

jump   ant   corn   cake   pig

1. Bob told his pals, "We have to stay near

_____"

_____.

| the path | my dad | this hill of mud |

2. Did the pals stay near the path? _____

| yes | no |

3. Did Bob stay near the path? _____

| yes | no |

4. Did Bob have mud in his ears? _____

| yes | no |

Name _____

1. Bob had to be home by _____ .

| three | five | nine |

2. A man said, "I see a hill of mud that
_____ "
_____ .

| can sit | can eat | can run |

3. Did Bob make it home by five? _____

| yes | no |

4. Will Bob have to stay at home for a

while? _____

| yes | no |

5. His dad said, "But you didn't stay near
_____ "
_____ .

| the lake | the cat | the path |

hill	<u>ea</u>r	r<u>oa</u>d	<u>ea</u>t

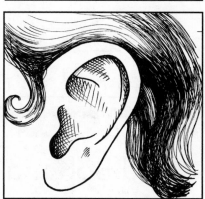

_____ kite _____ _____

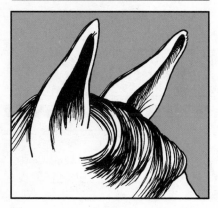

_____ r<u>u</u>g _____ _____

w<u>ay</u> •   • tray

m<u>ay</u> •   • my

we •   • way

my •   • dry

try •   • try

tr<u>ay</u> •   • we

dry •   • may

Name _____

1. The <u>othe</u>r d<u>ay</u>, we rode to a _____.
   - lake   - hill   - mill

2. The g<u>ear</u> w<u>a</u>s n<u>ear</u> a _____.
   - hill   - hive   - hat

3. I hav<u>e</u> a sore <u>ear</u> and a sore _____.
   - r<u>ear</u>   - t<u>ear</u>   - nose

4. My nam<u>e</u> is _____.
   - Dan   - Fran   - Ann

5. Can I h<u>ear</u>? _____
   - yes   - no

old note sick crow

 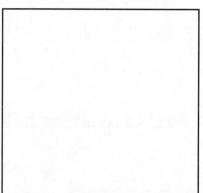 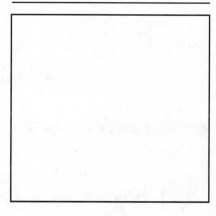

sun   pans

win	m<u>ea</u>n

with   mean   me

mean

will   win   won   meal

win

mean   win   win   win

mean   will

mean   win

man   with   mean   mean

Name _____

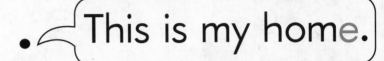

This is my home.

He dug a hole into the home.

He ate a bug.

And I can <u>eat</u> bugs if I feel like it.

I can make holes if I feel like it.

coat	five	run	train	sat

5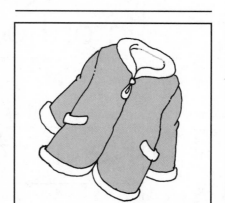

1. Did the **t<u>oa</u>d** like holes in his home?

_____

- - - - -

_____

• yes   • no

2. So the **t<u>oa</u>d** _____.

- ate the bug   • ran into a pal

- sat in the grass

I made it home
by five.

But you didn't stay
near the path.

fold

The Hill of Mud

Bob

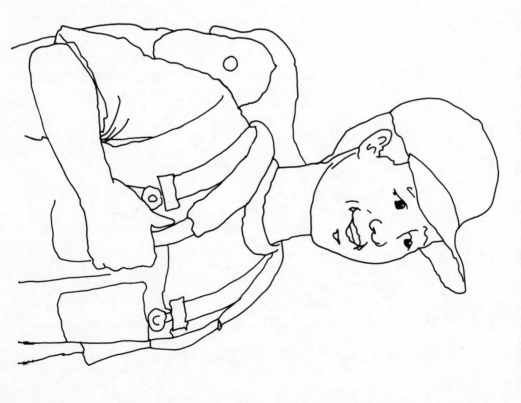

Yes, Bob, you may go. But you have to stay near the path. And you have to come home by five.

Dad, can I go for a hike with my pals?

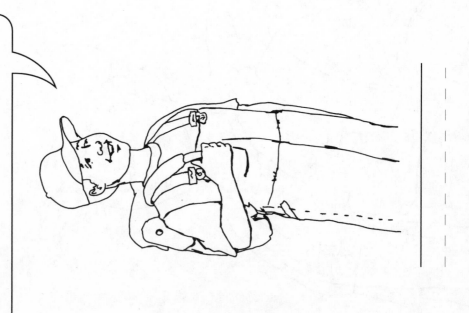

Name _____

1. I have to sit in _____.
   • my home   • a lake   • the rain

2. I wait for _____.
   • a cat   • my pal   • the sun

3. Is my pal late? _____
   • yes   • no

4. Do I see him at last? _____
   • yes   • no

5. Will we have fun? _____
   • yes   • no

stone tr<u>ai</u>l pigs fan pile cave

play	pal	hike	~~hive~~	(pals)
			3	4

pals   have   pill

hike   pal   hide   pals   hiked

hive   hill   hive   hits   plays

hid   have   pals   pal   hills

hid   play   hike   pals   have

hive   hide   pill   hid   pill

1. Who made the pals cold? _____
   • a pig   • a wind   • a cat

2. Who made a fire? _____
   • the pals   • the wind   • my dad

3. Did the fire get big? _____
   • yes   • no

spy	math	rak**e**
p<u>a</u>rk	s<u>oa</u>k<u>ed</u>	<u>wh</u>it**e**

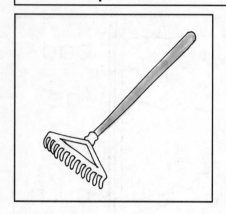

$$\begin{array}{r} 6 \\ + 3 \\ \hline \end{array}$$

<u>a</u>rm •　　　• grow

grass •　　　• grab

green •　　　• grass

grow •　　　• green

grab •　　　• _____

g<u>ea</u>r •————• _____

Name

fire   b<u>ar</u>n   pals

Ho, ho. It's time for a

_____
_____.

c<u>ar</u>   g<u>ea</u>r   seeds   <u>wh</u>eel

1. Who made a bad joke? _____
   • Bob   • the pals   • the wind

2. Who made the fire lick at the barn?
   _____
   _____
   • the wind   • the pals   • Bob

3. Will the pals save the barn from the fire?
   _____
   _____
   • yes   • no   • I don't know.

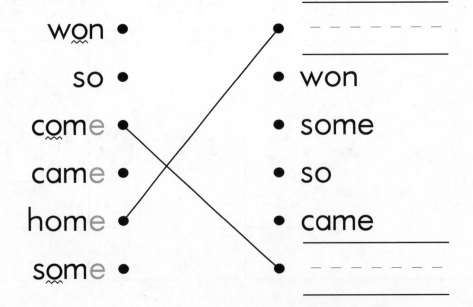

won •
so •
come •
came •
home •
some •

• won
• some
• so
• came

Name _____

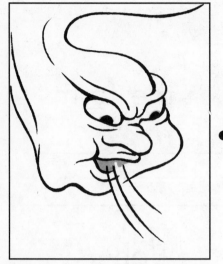

We like r**ai**n.

I will keep those flames aw**ay** from the b**ar**n.

I will blow big flames up the side **of** that b**ar**n.

I hate r**ai**n.

L**ea**ve this f**ar**m or I will s**oa**k you s**o**me more.

1. The m<u>ea</u>n wind made flam<u>e</u>s go up the

_____

side <u>of</u> _____.

• the b<u>ar</u>n   • the tree   • the f<u>ar</u>m

2. <u>Wh</u>at came from the sky? _____

• a fly   • r<u>ai</u>n   • Bob

| <u>o</u>ne | fire | bee | three | fi<u>sh</u> |

3

1

fi<u>sh</u>   _____   bee

Name _____

1. _____

2. _____

3. _____

1. with

2. <u>wh</u>ite

3. blow

4. f<u>ar</u>m

A Mole

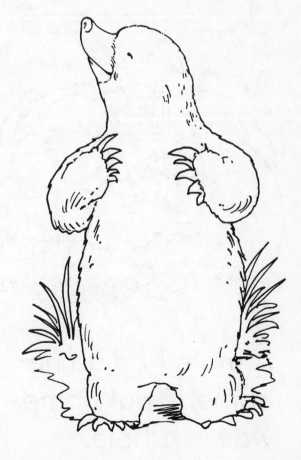

The mole likes to
_____
_____.

A toad had a fine home. A mean bug dug a hole into that home.

The toad said, "This is my home."

I have a fine
_____
‗ ‗ ‗ ‗ ‗ ‗ ‗ ‗
_____.

A mole had a fine home. That home was in a hole.

The mole played with cats at a lake. He had fun.

Name

tree   you   mole   fun   some   crow

Who a̰re _____?

I will have
_____
_____
_____ _____ .

1. <u>Wh</u>at did the mol<u>e</u> run int<u>o</u>?

_____

- - - - - - - - - - - - - - - - - - - -

_____

- • a hole   • a tree   • a crow

_____

2. Wh<u>o</u> was in the tree? _____

- • a mole   • a g<u>oa</u>t   • a crow

| fins | flame | hive | t<u>oa</u>d |

_____   _____   c<u>ar</u>

b<u>ar</u>n

_____

Side 2

Name _____

feet   hole   free   home

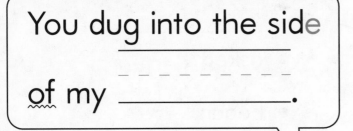
You dug into the side _____
of my _____.

I need to free _____
these _____.

1. Who told the mole what to do? _____

   • the tree   • the snake   • the crow

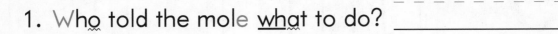

2. The mole said, "I dig, dig, dig, but these feet are too _____"
   _____.

   • old, old, old   • deep   • big, big, big

3. The mole came to the home of a wise _____.

   • duck   • snake   • man

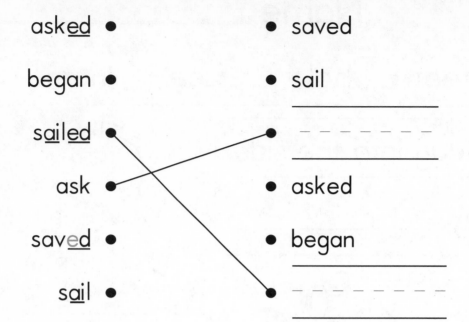

asked •   • saved

began •   • sail

sailed •   • _____

ask •   • _ _ _ _ _ _

saved •   • asked

sail •   • began

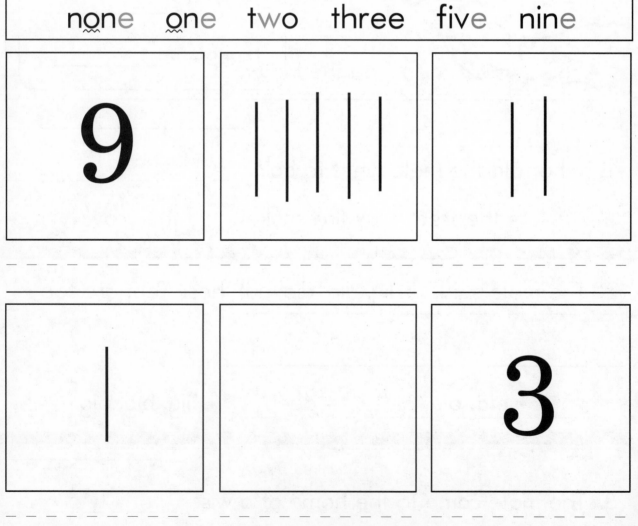

none   one   two   three   five   nine

Name _____

the mole   the snake

1. Who was trying to free the big one?

_____

_____

2. Who told the mole that she was digging under a tree?

_____

_____

3. Who said, "I think I know what to do"?

_____

_____

4. Do you think the snake will play a joke?

_____

_____

drive blow <u>sh</u>ip sting d<u>ar</u>k t<u>ai</u>ls

_____

_____

told •   • or
                         _____
for •   • _____
                         _____
hold •   • old

or •   • cold

cold •   • for

old •   • told

Name _____

| gold   mole   big one   crow |

1. Who told the crow that the big one was stuck in gold?

_____

- - - - - - - - - - - -

_____

2. Who slid into the hole the mole had dug?

_____

- - - - - - - - - - - -

_____

3. What did the crow see in the hole?

_____

- - - - - - - - - - - -

_____

4. Do you think the crow will take gold from the hole?

_____

- - - - - - - - - - - -

_____

• yes   • no   • I don't know.

5. Do you think the gold is part of the joke?

_____

- - - - - - - - - - - -

_____

• yes   • no

cake b<u>ar</u>n ring four sky stor<u>e</u>s

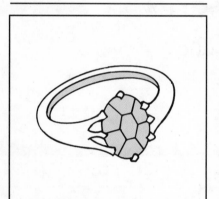

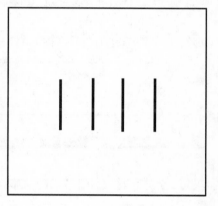

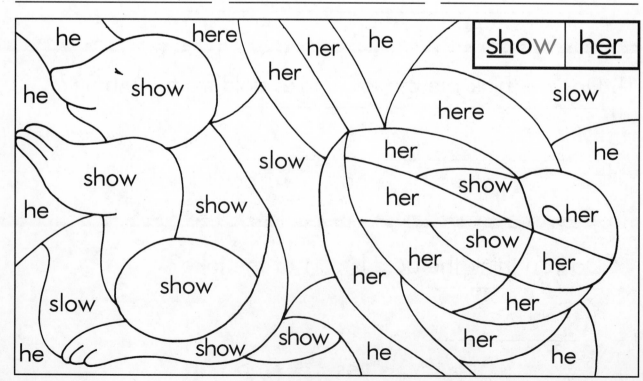

<u>sh</u>ow | h<u>er</u>

Name _____

mole   snake   gold   crow

You can have the
_____
_____ .

1. As the crow started to grab for the gold, it became
_____
_____ .   • dark   • big   • old

2. Did the crow grab the lump of gold? _____

3. Who said, "Shame on you for playing jokes on moles"?
_____
_____

4. Did the crow stop playing jokes on moles? _____

hat   hit   pl<u>ay</u>   f<u>a</u>rm   sing   m<u>o</u>th<u>e</u>r

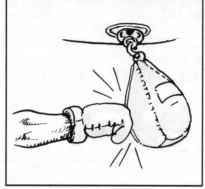

_____

_____

cold •

come •

note •

not •

on •

no •

• not

_____

• cold

_____

• come

• note

I have a sore ear but I
can hear. And I have a

rear. So I
can't sit.

From Ann

fold

Note to Dad

Dear Dad,
The other day we rode
bikes to a lake. We ate and
played games.

I had my gear near a bee
hive. Those mean bees gave
me some tears.

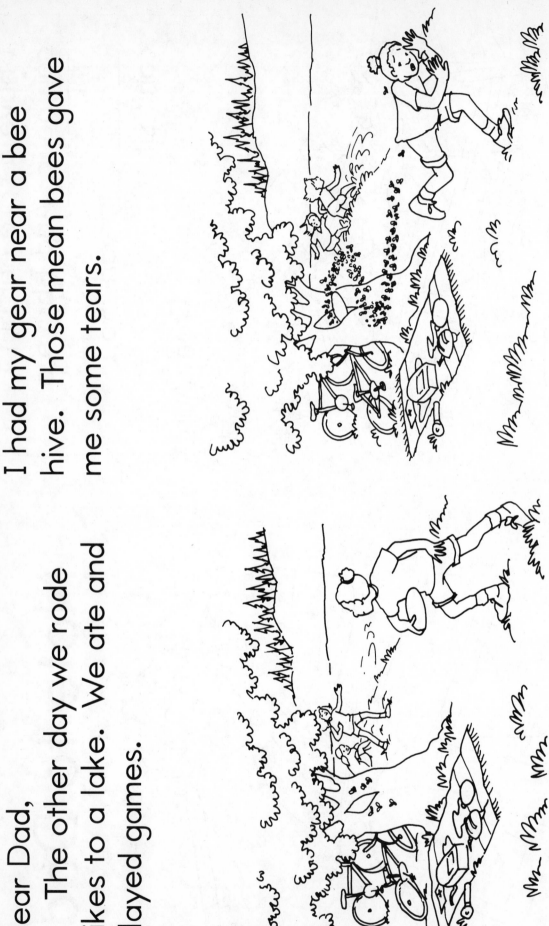

Name _____

pig   corn   g<u>oa</u>t   cow

pile of _____

1. <u>Wh</u>at did the pig and the g<u>oa</u>t lik<u>e</u> to do? _____

   • sit   • <u>ea</u>t   • sleep

2. <u>Who</u> told the pig and g<u>oa</u>t to st<u>a</u>rt <u>ea</u>ting?

   _____   • Bob   • a crow   • a cow

3. <u>Who</u> ate fast<u>er</u>? _____

A <u>Sh</u>ip and a Fi<u>sh</u> •

Digging and Sleeping •

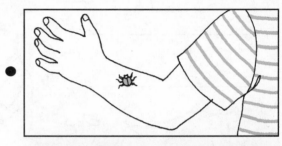

A Bug on an <u>A</u>rm •

A G<u>oa</u>t and a Cr<u>ow</u> •

A‾‾‾‾‾‾‾‾‾‾‾‾‾‾ •

wait   leap   those

rain   over   away

Name _____

I _____ for

my _____ .

rain
pal
hate
wait

1. Did the sun <u>shine</u>? _____

2. <u>Wh</u>at p<u>a</u>rts wer<u>e</u> s<u>oa</u>k<u>ed</u>? _____

   • c<u>oa</u>t and hat   • c<u>oa</u>t and t<u>ai</u>l   • t<u>ai</u>l and m<u>ai</u>l

3. <u>Wh</u>at did the pals plan to do? _____

   _____

   • have a m<u>ea</u>l   • have s<u>o</u>m<u>e</u> gum   • have s<u>o</u>m<u>e</u> fun

4. <u>Wh</u><u>o</u> is the pal? _____

s̲he   w̲h̲eels   s̲h̲op   wav̲e   teeth   f̲a̲rm

_____   _____   _____

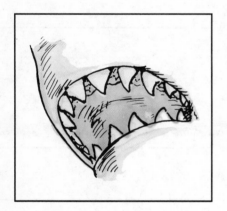  

_____   _____   _____

this   coat   wait

read   while   farm

Name _____

1. Who started the fire? _____

   • Bob   • the pals   • the mean wind

2. Who made the flames leap up the side of the barn?
   _____

   • Bob   • the pals   • the mean wind

3. Who soaked the fire? _____

   • Bob   • the rain   • the mean wind

4. Do you like the rain? _____

mean	farm	start
wish	leave	day

mat	p<u>a</u>rk	line	lines
<u>a</u>rm	king	fi<u>sh</u>	stove

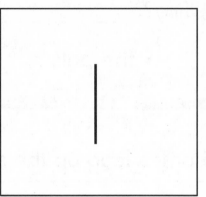

_____

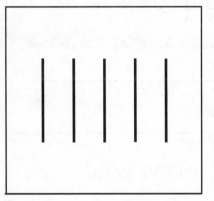

_____

_____

Name _____

ship   gold   shop

I will take the _____
from her.

1. Pam lived _____.

    • in a home   • on a ship   • on a hill

2. In her shop she had _____.

    • gold   • corn   • goats

3. Who said, "I think I will sneak into that ship"?

    • Bob   • a robber   • a snake

car   folding   hurt

cop   bird   cash

over ●   ● mother

under ●   ● her

other ●   ● here

mother ●   ● other

here ●   ● over

her ●   ● under

Side 2

Name _____

1. _____

2. _____

3. _____

 1. stopp<u>ed</u>

2. <u>wh</u>at

3. b<u>ar</u>n

4. b<u>ur</u>n

1. Who ate more corn?

_____

_____

2. Who ate faster?

_____

_____

3. The goat and the

_____

_____ got mad.

Corn for Three

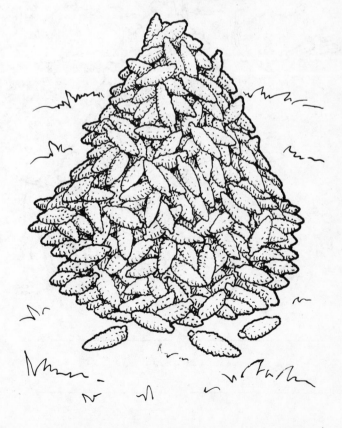

Side 1

One d<u>ay</u>, a g<u>oa</u>t and a pig wer<u>e</u> pl<u>ay</u>ing n<u>ea</u>r a pil<u>e</u> of corn. The g<u>oa</u>t said, "I can <u>ea</u>t that corn."

The pig said, "Me too."

The goat said, "I can eat faster than you."

The pig said, "You can not."

A cow said, "Why don't you start eating and see who wins?"

So the goat and the pig started to eat the corn.

The cow said, "I think I will eat some corn too."

Side 2

Name _____

I can't pick up this _____.

gold
lump
up
lamp

1. Who came to take the gold? _____

   • a robber   • Bob   • Pam

2. Did the robber see the gold? _____

3. _____ cops came into the shop.

   • Two
   • Three
   • Four

4. What was made of gold? _____

   • a lump   • a lamp   • a camp

<u>sh</u><u>ir</u>t	teeth	hat
clock	corn	b<u>ar</u>king

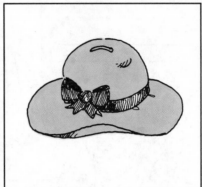

bring •   •

thing •   • hearing

hid<u>ing</u> •   • kicked

h<u>ea</u>ring •   • hiked

hik<u>ed</u> •   • hiding

kick<u>ed</u> •   •

Name

I need some sweet
_____
_ _ _ _ _ _ _ _ _ _
_____ .

batter
bitter
butter

_____
_ _ _ _ _ _ _ _ _ _
My butter is _____ .

robber   napped   hiker   started   stirred   stinger

1. Who asked for a cake? _____

   • the mom turtle   • the fox   • the little turtle

2. What did the mom need for the cake?

   _____

   • sweet bitter   • sweet butter   • sweet grass

3. The mom gave the little turtle some _____.

   • cake   • cash   • cans

4. Who stopped the little turtle near the farm?

   _____

5. Did the fox say that he had sweet butter?

   _____

6. The butter that the fox had was _____.

   • sweet   • batter   • bitter

Name

Can I taste that _____ ?

fox
cake
mom

town   ship   darts   barn   clock   cold

1. Who sold butter to the little turtle?

_____

- - - - - - - - - - - - - - - - -

_____

- the black fox   - the red fox   - the brown fox

2. Who made the batter? _____

- - - - - - - - - - - - - - - - -

- mom   - Bob   - the little turtle

3. What did the turtles do while the cake baked?

_____

- - - - - - - - - - - - - - - - -

_____

- played   - waited   - ate

4. Who tasted the cake first? _____

- - - - - - - - - - - - - - - - -

- mom   - Bob   - the little turtle

5. Was the cake sweet? _____

- - - - - - - - - - -

cash   soap   trails

play   start   white

Name

fox
cak**e**
butter

hill f**ar**m s**ea**t **ar**ms cak**e** hot

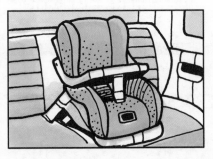

1. Was the butter sweet or bitter? _____

2. How did the butter make the cake taste?
_____
_____

3. Who tasted the cake first? _____

  • mom   • Bob   • the little turtle

4. Who tasted the cake next? _____

5. Who did the turtles plan to see? _____

  • the crow   • the big one   • the fox

turn   coats   cash   hard

really   path   paint

Name _____

it   bitter   like

I _____ ___.

1. Who did the turtles visit? _____

• the fox   • Bob   • the big one

2. What did the turtles bring the fox?

_____   • gold   • cash   • a cake

3. Was that cake sweet? _____

4. How did that cake taste? _____

5. How was the fox going to eat the cake?

_____   • slowly   • fast   • not too slowly

| cash | s<u>oa</u>ked | pond | rocks | box | <u>ch</u>air |

  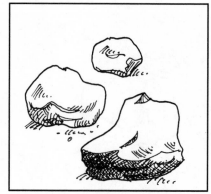

over   maybe   dirty

chase   card   shame

train   throw

Side 2

One cop grabbed the lamp. He
said, "I can't pick up this lamp."
The other cop said, "I know why
you can't pick it up. It's made of gold.
Ho, ho, ho."

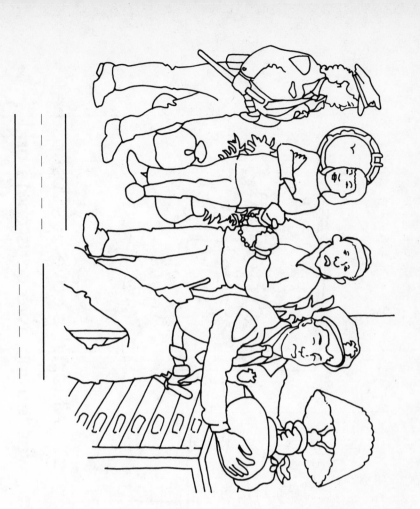

fold

How Pam Hid
Her Gold

Pam had a shop on her ship.
One thing in that shop was lots of
gold.

A robber got into her shop to

take the gold.

He said, "I see sacks and rocks

and clocks. And I see a big lamp. But

I see no gold."

At last, he gave up. Just as he

was leaving, two cops came and

grabbed him.

Later, the cops asked Pam, "Can

you show us how you hide the

gold?"

She said, "If you pick up the big

lamp, you will know how I hide the

gold."

Name _____

fox
turtles
pond

I see goats and bugs. ●

●

Two goats ate grass. ●

●

A turtle mixed batter. ●

●

1. Who ate the cake? _____

   • the fox   • Bob   • the big one

2. How did the cake taste? _____

3. After the fox ate the cake, he said, "I need something _____ "
_____.

   • to eat   • to see   • to drink

4. He ran to the _____.

   • town   • pond   • farm

5. Did he dive in? _____

6. Did the cake leave a bad taste? _____

Name _____

summer   ride   birds

It feels like
_____
_____ .

I am going to see the
_____
_____ .

She rocked the baby. ●

Mother ate the chips. ●

The fox licked a box. ●

1. What was the winter like?

_____

- -

_____

- hard and hot   - hard and cold   - hotter and hotter

2. Who said, "I will ride my bike to the lake"?

_____

- - - - - - - - - - - -

_____   - Bob   - Irma   - Vern

3. What did Irma plan to see? _____

- - - - - - - - - - - - - - - -

_____

- birds   - a hill of mud   - goats

4. Who wore a big hat? _____

- - - - - - - - - -

_____

5. What was the only thing Vern wore?

_____

- -

_____

- socks   - a big hat   - short pants

Name _____

sun   Vern   lake   beach

rocks   bike   spring   happy   ship   chair   brother   winter

      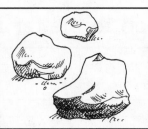   

1. How did Vern and Irma get to the lake?

_____

- - - - - - - - - - - - - - - -

_____

- on boats   - on bikes   - in a car

2. Which one was as white as snow? _____

_____

- - - - - - - - -

- Bob   - Vern   - the little turtle

3. Which shore did Vern like?

_____

- - - - - - - - - - - - - - - -

_____

- the shore with shade   - the sandy shore

4. Who liked the shore with birds? _____

_____

- - - - - - - - -

5. Why did Irma go to the far shore?

_____

- - - - - - - - - - - - - - - -

_____

- to see birds   - to swim   - to sleep

Name _____

1. Who stayed at the sandy beach? _____

2. Did Vern stay in the shade? _____

3. At first, Vern turned _____.

    • very pink   • a little pink   • red

4. When Vern got home, he was _____.

5. Who asked him why he didn't take a hat and a shirt?
_____

_____

    • Bob   • his mother   • Al

6. Vern said, "I didn't _____."

    • think   • stink   • pink

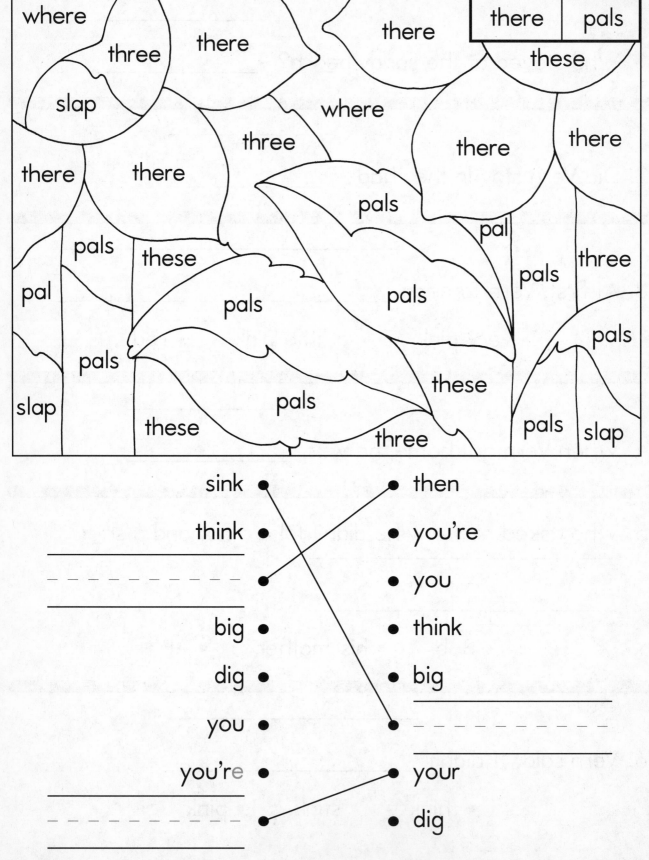

where

three

slap

there

pal

slap

there

three

there

pals

pals

these

pals

these

pals

there

where

three

these

pals

pals

pals

three

there

there

these

pal

pals

there

pals

three

pals

slap

there	pals

these

sink

think

big

dig

you

you're

then

you're

you

think

big

your

dig

Name _____

1. _____
2. _____
3. _____

1. became
2. hurry
3. other
4. swim
5. drink

fold

The big turtle said, "I had a sun bath. Now I will have a rain bath. Ho, ho."

Two brown turtles lived in the weeds near a pond. One day the turtles were sitting on some rocks. The big turtle said, "I really like this sun."

Side 1

The mom turtle began to make the batter. She said, "We mix sweet butter into the batter."

But she had bitter butter. And bitter butter won't make a sweet cake.

After a while, the sky became darker. The little turtle said, "I think it will start to rain. Maybe we need to go home."

But the big turtle said, "No. I will stay here. The sun will come back."

The sun did not come back. Rain came down.

Name

pail   goat   fox   toad   pig

mom •   • something to sit in

pond •   • someone's mother

bitter •   • a little lake

chair •   • ants and bees

bugs •   • it tastes bad

1. Did Gorman like to play with his pals? _____

2. Did the pals like to play with Gorman? _____

3. What w<u>ere</u> his pals playing with? _____

   • a ram   • a pail   • a boat

4. Wh<u>o</u> said, "I may be the best pail jumper there is"?

   _____

   _____

   • the f<u>ar</u>mer   • Bob   • Gorman

5. Wh<u>o</u> did Gorman run into? _____

   • the f<u>ar</u>mer   • the pig   • the crow

soap	pals	slap	there		~~pals~~	(there)
these	maps	pans	those	there	3	4
soap	pal	lips	where	three	the	pals
there	lips	naps	here	where		slap
then	pans	the	last	those	slap	then	pans
here	pal	pals		these		there

Name _____

1. Who was Tom? _____

      • an otter   • a shark   • his dad

2. Did Tom listen to his mom and dad? _____

3. At first, he followed a clam that _____ .

    • was stinking   • was sinking   • was pink

4. Then he followed seals for _____ .

    • ten weeks   • a mile or more   • after he got sore

5. What did Tom see near the weeds? _____

    • a seal   • his mom   • a shark

shark •   • something that is burning

bike •   • what you h<u>ea</u>r with

fan •   • something that blows air on you

fire •   • a big fish with lots of teeth

<u>e</u>ars •   • it has two wheels

~~any~~	thing
4	3

sinking   think   bring   any

an   am   any   many

think   thing   things

an   sting   any   thin   thing

think   many   funny   any

thing   an   this   many

hurt   yell   chase   shore   swim   pants

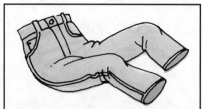

Name _____

Tom   got   mom   sh<u>ar</u>k   weeds

I've _____ you now.

Not.

Many fish swam in a pond. ●   ●

A sh<u>ar</u>k chased his tail. ●   ●

A seal was on the beach. ●   ●

1. Which otter yelled from beneath?

_____

\- \- \- \- \- \- \- \- \- \- \- \-

_____

- Tom   • Tom's mom   • Tom's dad

2. Who bit the shark's tail? _____

3. Which otter did the shark chase?

_____

\- \- \- \- \- \- \- \- \- \- \- \-

_____

4. Tom's mom stopped

_____

\- \- \- \- \- \- \- \- \- \- \- \- \- \-

_____.

- in a cave   • in front of a rock   • to eat

5. Was Tom shocked? _____

farm •	• jump
hive •	• lots of speed
easy •	• a home for cows, sheep and goats
leap •	• a home for bees
fast •	• not hard

Side 2

Name _____

A bird is on my <u>arm</u>. ●

Which trail do we take? ●

A cop met a mole. ●

1. Where did Tom's mom stop?

_____

- - - - - - - - - - - - - - - - - - -

_____

    • in a cave   • in front of a rock

2. Who saved Tom?

    • his mom   • a seal   • Bob

3. What did the shark run into?

    • Bob   • a rock   • a cave

4. Does that shark know that he is a shark?

5. What does the shark think he is?

    • a seal   • a meal   • Bob

Name

☐ 1. Make a **T** over the tree.

☐ 2. Make an **O** under the tree.

☐ 3. Make a **T** on the side of the fish.

1. How f<u>ar</u> from town was Jill's f<u>ar</u>m?

_____

- - - - - - - - - - - - - - -

_____

    • I don't know.   • three miles   • six miles

2. Where did she need to go? _____

    • to the f<u>ar</u>m   • to the store   • to see Bob

3. How did she get there? _____

- hike
- run
- drive

4. Wh<u>o</u> was going to pick her up? _____

    • Bob   • her mother   • her dad

5. What was her dad driving? _____

    • a c<u>ar</u>   • a tract<u>or</u>   • a trailer

skunk		star		10			star
			9				7
	star	blue			skunk		
thank		dear		star	sunk		

Side 2

Tom and the Shark

There once was an otter and his name was Tom.
But Tom didn't listen to his dad or mom.

One day his mom told him, "Don't swim near the caves.
Because there's a shark who hunts in those waves."

But Tom started playing and he wasn't really thinking.
He first chased a clam that seemed to be sinking.

Then he followed two seals that were close to the shore.
He followed those seals for a mile or more.

At last he stopped to see where he was.
He said, "I saw something swimming the way a shark does."

"Oh, oh," he said, as he hid near a weed.
"I hope this is not where sharks like to feed."

But the shark came closer and showed many teeth.
And just at that moment someone yelled from beneath.

"For a bigger meal, you can come after me."
The otter who spoke was Tom's mom, you see,

She swam and she dove and bit the shark's tail.
She told that shark, "You're as slow as a snail."

The shark chased Tom's mom as fast as a shot.
And said, "I've got you now." But Tom's mom said, "Not."

Just then Tom got a very bad shock.
His mom just stopped, in front of a rock.

As the shark came closer did she stay where she was?
No, she darted to one side, the way an otter does.

The shark hit the rock with such a hard blow,
That he said to himself, "Who am I? I do not know."

Then he asked Tom's mom, "Can you tell me who I am?"
She said, "You're a very big seal, and your name is Sam."

So Tom has a pal who thinks he's a seal.
And Sam doesn't know that Tom is a meal.

The end.

Name

tractor   steer   field

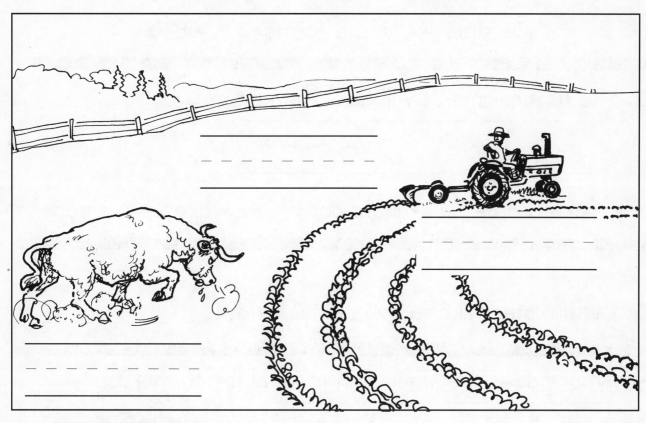

1. triangle

2. box

3. circle

☐ 1. Make an e in the circle.

☐ 2. Make a b on top of the circle.

☐ 3. Make a T over the triangle.

☐ 4. Make a J under the box.

1. Who lived in a field? _____

    • a steer   • the farmer   • Bob

2. The farmer said, "I will dig. Then I can
_____ "
_____ .

    • make a hole   • plant corn   • wake up a steer

3. Did the steer like farmers in his field? _____

4. Where does the steer plan to send the farmer?
_____
_____

    • to a lake   • to his field   • to his home

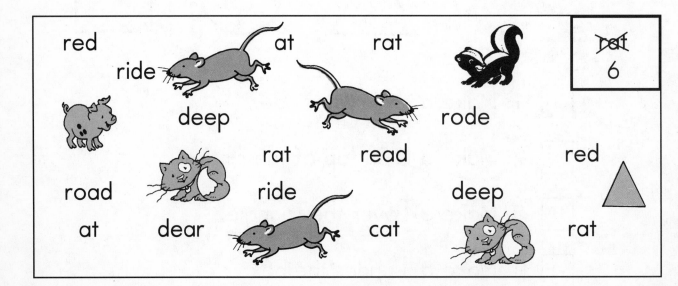

red   at   rat

ride   rode

deep   rat   read   red

road   ride   deep

at   dear   cat   rat

~~rat~~
6

Side 2

Name _____

1. circle   2. box   3. triangle

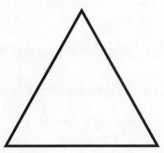

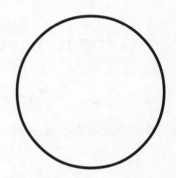

1. Make a **d** inside the triangle.
2. Make an **i** over the circle.
3. Make a **t** under the box.
4. Make a fish inside the circle.
5. Make a turtle inside the box.

b**a**lls   beach   smil**e**   otter   digging   bells

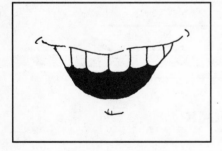

1. Where were the farmer and the steer?

_____

- - - - - - - - - - - - - - - -

_____

  • in a field   • in a barn   • in Bob's home

2. Who ran into the tractor? _____

  • a steer   • a goat   • a farmer

3. Who went flying? _____

4. The steer landed on its _____.

  • feet   • seat   • back

5. The steer said, "I see _____."

6. The steer said, "I hear _____."

Side 2

Name

1. Circle the fish.
2. Box the seal.
3. Box the bird.
4. Make an h under the tail of the fish.
5. Make an i over a box.

1. How many pigs did Pam have? _____

2. What was the name of the small pig? _____

3. Did Pam have pig feed? _____

4. She planned to feed the pigs _____.
   • pig feed   • dog chow   • hot peppers

5. Were some of the peppers in a pan? _____

the front of a car •

driving a car •

loading a trailer •

planting seeds •

~~any~~	cup
4	5

Side 2

Name

Pig
Pam
Six
Burp

1. Make a **U** in front of the bird.

2. Make a **5** in back of the car.

3. Circle the barn.

4. Box the bird.

1. How many pigs turned red? _____

2. Where did the red pigs go first?
_____
_____
_____

• the drinking pan • the barn • the field

3. Which pig did not turn red? _____

4. Which pig ate a lot of peppers? _____

5. Did Pig Six like those peppers? _____

6. What does Pig Six do to say "thank you"?
_____
_____
_____

• eats dirt • b<u>ur</u>ps • yells

Name _____

1. _____

2. _____

3. _____

4. _____

1. drink	6. became
2. here	7. many
3. turned	8. where
4. were	9. leaving
5. drank	10. never

At last she saw him. Was he driving the car? No. He was driving a tractor with a trailer.

Jill loaded her bags into the trailer and her dad drove her home.

The end.

fold

_____

Jill lived on a farm that was six miles from town.

Pam had red hot peppers. She had piles of peppers.

She said, "I think I'll feed these peppers to my pigs. Those pigs eat everything."

So she loaded some peppers in a pot and a pan.

Jill told her dad, "It is time to go to the store."

"Well," her dad said, "I need to fix the car. So I can't drive you there now."

Jill said, "I have a plan. I can hike to the store. Later, you can pick me up."

So Jill hiked to the store. When she got there, she got a cart and filled it. Then she waited for her dad in front of the store. He didn't show up. Then she began to think of things that may have made her dad late.